The Self-Reflection Habit

the key to leadership self-awareness

Rudy Sprogis, PCC

L E A D E

Leadership begins with knowing what you're doing, why you're doing it, and how you're doing it.

That's why outstanding leaders make self-awareness a priority and self-reflection a daily habit.

Self-reflection gives you insight into how you work—what you do well and what needs improving.

Let's face it, none of us likes to admit that we don't have all the answers—that we made a mistake or that we could have done something better.

Leaders who don't take the time to reflect, however, risk making the same mistakes over and over again.

In order to be effective, self-reflection requires you to be honest—to sharply question yourself and your behavior.

R S H I P

Research shows that it takes 66 days before a new behavior becomes a habit.

On the following pages, I present 66 essential questions to help you develop **The Self-Reflection Habit**.

My clients use these questions between visits for self-reflection and learning.

Dedicate fifteen minutes each day to answering one of the questions posed throughout this leadership journal, using the pages provided.

Take an honest look at yourself–your strengths *and* your weaknesses.

This daily practice of self-reflection and journaling will build your self-awareness, helping you to grow and develop into an exceptional leader.

Rudy Sprogis, PCC

If this leadership journal helps you in some way, I'd love to hear about it.

Email me:
rudy@rudysprogis.com

"The hardest person you will ever have to lead is yourself"

– BILL GEORGE

01

what is it to be a leader?

02

what is it to be powerful?

03

what are my strengths?

04

what are my challenges?

"What you do has far greater impact than what you say"

–STEPHEN R. COVEY

05

what is integrity?

06

what do I pretend?

07

what is my reputation?

"The function of leadership is to produce more leaders, not more followers"

– RALPH NADER

08

what am I building?

09

what do I want?

10

what do I expect of myself?

11

what is my vision for myself?

12

what motivates me?

13

what is stopping me?

"Character, not circumstances, makes the man"

– BOOKER T. WASHINGTON

14

what do I value?

15

what am I grateful for?

16

what rules should I be breaking?

17

what is the difference between a wish and a goal?

18

what are my wants versus my musts?

19

what do I need in order to reach my goals?

"As a leader your every action has a consequence, make sure it is one you intend"

– KATHERINE BRYANT

20

how do I respond to change?

21

how do I respond to conflict?

22

how do I respond to stress?

23

how do I respond to uncertainty?

24

what's working?

25

what isn't working?

26

what do I need to do differently?

"Give light and people will find the way"

– ELLA BAKER

27

when am I at my best?

28

what skills do I need to learn?

29

what skills do I need to practice?

30

what am I choosing?

31

what am I allowing?

32

where is my attention?

33

what keeps me on track?

34

what pulls me off course?

35

what keeps me from winning?

"Leadership is a series of behaviors rather than a role for heroes"

– MARGARET J. WHEATLEY

36

how do I sabotage myself?

37

where do I give my power away –and to whom?

38

where am I asleep at the wheel?

39

what am I afraid of?

40

what am I willing to risk?

41

what am I unwilling to risk?

42

where am I holding back?

43

what am I settling for?

44

what am I tolerating?

"To handle yourself, use your head; to handle others, use your heart"

– ELEANOR ROOSEVELT

45

what am I resisting?

46

where do I limit myself?

47

where am I
too flexible?

48

where am I uncompromising?

49

when am I unable to laugh at myself?

50

what am I being right about?

51

where am I too hard on myself?

52

what do I need to leave alone?

53

what am I unwilling to change?

54

what am I willing to change?

"The growth and development of people is the highest calling of leadership"

– HARVEY S. FIRESTONE

55

what have I built?

56

how far have I come?

57

what did it take to get here?

58

what have I learned about myself?

59

who have I become?

60

how do I measure success?

61

how do I acknowledge my accomplishments?

"Don't follow the crowd, let the crowd follow you"

– MARGARET THATCHER

62

what's next?

63

what's my mission?

64

what's the dream?

65

what's possible?

66

what is my contribution to the world going to be?

"A boss has the title. A leader has the people."

— SIMON SINEK

Thank You

To Patrick ... for the encouragement

To Caroline McArthur at whitefox ... for humoring me when I say "FINAL"

To Doug Kerr at Studio Doug ... for saying "yes"

To Karen Salmansohn ... for the exclamation points

To my friends and family ... for spreading the word

Rudy Sprogis, PCC is a credential-holder with the International Coaching Federation (ICF) and an award-winning salon leadership coach. He has been featured in numerous consumer and trade publications including American Salon, Modern Salon and Salon Today magazines. For over a decade, Sprogis has been coaching beauty industry professionals to build self-awareness, clarify goals and improve performance.

Made in the USA
Middletown, DE
22 July 2021